Tricking the Tiger

A play by Julia Donaldson

Illustrated by Garry Parsons

Characters

Mrs Fox

Tiger

Girl Fox

2

Mr Fox

Boy Fox

Narrator

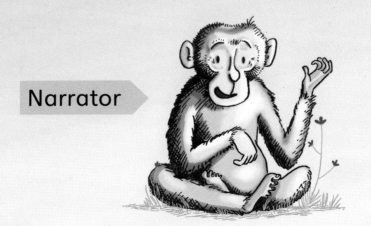

3

Narrator:	One sunny day, the Fox family set off for a walk.
Mr Fox:	But look out for Tiger!
Mrs Fox:	He likes eating foxes.
Narrator:	Soon, Tiger spotted them.
Tiger:	Aha! A family of foxes!

Boy Fox: Help! Tiger!

Girl Fox: Quick! Run!

Mr Fox: No, he's too fast. We'll have to trick him instead.

Girl Fox: But how?

Mrs Fox: I know! Listen carefully. We need to pretend that we have three extra cubs back in the den.

Boy Fox: Why?

Mr Fox: Don't ask questions.

Mrs Fox: There's no time to explain.

Girl Fox: Just do what Mum says.

Boy Fox: Help! Here comes Tiger!

Narrator: Tiger prowled up.

Tiger: Good morning, foxes. Isn't it a beautiful day?

Mrs Fox: I suppose so.

Tiger: You don't sound very happy. What's the problem?

Mrs Fox: The problem is that we have too many fox cubs.

Mr Fox: Yes, there are five of them.

Girl Fox: The other three are back in the den.

Boy Fox: *(whispering)* But we don't have any other brothers and sisters!

Girl Fox: *(whispering)* We've got to pretend we have.

Tiger: Five fox cubs! That doesn't sound like a problem to me!

Mrs Fox: The problem is, we don't know how to feed them all.

Mr Fox: That's right. There are five hungry mouths to feed.

Mrs Fox: Seven, if you count the two of us as well, dear.

Boy Fox: What are Mum and Dad talking about?

Girl Fox: *(whispering)* They're just pretending!

Narrator: Tiger could hardly believe his luck.

Tiger: I think I might be able to help you. I have lots of food in my den. Why don't you come to tea?

Mr Fox: What, all of us?

Girl Fox: Even the other three cubs?

Boy Fox: *(whispering)* But there aren't any other cubs!

Girl Fox: Shush!

Tiger: Yes, you can all come.

Mr Fox: Oh, thank you!

Mrs Fox: Let's go and fetch the others now.

Tiger: I'll come with you.

Narrator: So Tiger followed the foxes back home.

Girl Fox: Here we are!

Tiger: Excellent! Shall I go in and fetch the cubs?

Boy Fox: No!

Mrs Fox: No, you're too big. The other cubs can fetch them. In you go, you two.

Narrator: Boy Fox and Girl Fox disappeared into the den. The others waited.

Mrs Fox: Perhaps Mr Fox should go in and hurry them up.

Mr Fox: Good idea!

Narrator: Mr Fox disappeared into the den too.

Mrs Fox: Hurry up, you lot!

Tiger: Maybe they've forgotten. You'd better go in and remind them.

Mrs Fox: Good idea!

Narrator: Mrs Fox disappeared into the den. Tiger waited ...

and waited ...

and waited.

19

Tiger:	Come on out!
Boy Fox:	No!
Mrs Fox:	Here we are and here we stay!
Mr Fox:	Even if you wait all day!
Girl Fox:	I think you'd better go away!
Tiger:	Oh no! I've been tricked!